El Niño

SUIL FI ANNA CHONTAE NA AILLIMHE

Fiona MacDonald

OXFORD
UNIVERSITY PRESS

OXFORD
UNIVERSITY PRESS

Great Clarendon Street, Oxford OX2 6DP

Oxford University Press is a department of the University of Oxford.
It furthers the University's objective of excellence in research, scholarship,
and education by publishing worldwide in

Oxford New York

Athens Auckland Bangkok Bogotá Buenos Aires Calcutta
Cape Town Chennai Dar es Salaam Delhi Florence Hong Kong Istanbul
Karachi Kuala Lumpur Madrid Melbourne Mexico City Mumbai
Nairobi Paris São Paulo Singapore Taipei Tokyo Toronto Warsaw

with associated companies in Berlin Ibadan

Published in the United Kingdom
by Oxford University Press

First published 2000

British Library Cataloguing in Publication Data

Data available

ISBN 0 19 915709 X

Available in packs
Weather Pack of Six   (one of each book)   ISBN 0 19 915711 1
Weather Class Pack   (six of each book)   ISBN 0 19 915712 X

Printed in Hong Kong

Acknowledgements

The Publisher would like to thank the following for permission
to reproduce photographs:

National Aeronautics and Space Administration: p 12; National Geographic Society/ Image
Collection/Thad Samuels Abell: Cover, p 10; National Geographic Society/ Image
Collection/James Sugar:contents page, p 9 (*bottom*); National Geographic Society/ Image
Collection/NOAA/U.S. Government Commerce: p 5; National Geographic Society/ Image
Collection/Raymond K. Gehman: p 13 (*bottom*); Frank Lane Picture Library/W. Wisniewski: p 9
(*top*); Frank Lane Picture Library/Australian Information Service: p 13 (*top*); Frank Lane Picture
Library/C. Carvalho: p 14 (*top*); Joanna Pinneo 1999 / Aurora: p.6 (bottom left); Science Photo
Library/Peter Menzel: p 15 (*bottom*); South American Pictures/Tony Morrison: p 6 (*top*), 7(*top*);
Still Pictures/Gerard and Margi Moss: Cover inset, p 12 (*bottom*); Still Pictures/Edward Parker:
p 7 (*bottom*); Still Pictures/Tantyo Bangun: p 11 (*bottom*); Still Pictures /G. Griffiths/Christian
Aid: p 15 (*top*);

Illustrations by Janet Baker, Julian Baker, Tony Morris, and Olive Pearson.

Contents

What is El Niño?

El Niño is a **current** of warm water.
It flows across the Pacific Ocean and
along the coast of South America. It
appears once every four or five years.

The warm El
Niño **current**
is coloured
red on this
map.

NORTH AMERICA

N

China   Japan

Pacific

Equator

Ocean

Peru

SOUTH AMERICA

Australia

New Zealand

0   1000 km

1900–1901
1902–1903
1911–1912
1914–1915
1918–1919
1940–1941
1951–1952
1957–1958
1965–1966
1969–1970
1972–1973
1977–1978
1982–1983
1986–1987
1991–1992
1993–1994
1997–1998

1900   1910   1920   1930   1940   1950   1960   1970   1980   1990   2000

The El Niño current has appeared 17 times since 1900.

The Pacific Ocean has the biggest waves in the world. They help the weak winds change the **currents**.

Scientists think that El Niño is caused by changes in the wind. The winds that blow across the Pacific Ocean get weaker. The weak winds change the way the ocean **currents** flow.

FACT BOX

"El Niño" is a very old name. It was invented over 400 years ago by fishermen in Peru. They noticed that the warm current appeared around Christmas time. So they called it "El Niño", which means "Baby Boy".

Problems in Peru

The El Niño **current** flows
close to the coast of Peru.
It causes many problems for
people and wildlife living
there. It brings thick **fog**
and heavy rain.

Fog and rain
make it difficult
to go fishing.

The rain kills
crops, and washes
the soil from the
fields away.

Rain causes
mudslides which
sweep down the
mountains. This
woman's house
was washed
away in 1998.

At sea, El Niño's warm water kills tiny creatures called **plankton**. The fish that feed on the plankton starve and die. The birds that feed on the fish can die too.

There are no fish for fishermen and their families to catch and sell. They have no money to buy food.

These birds cannot find any fish to eat.

In El Niño years, Peruvian fishermen come back from fishing trips with much smaller catches than usual.

Droughts and floods

El Niño changes the weather in many parts of the world. In El Niño years, no rain falls for many months in Africa and Australia. There are long **droughts**, so many plants and animals die.

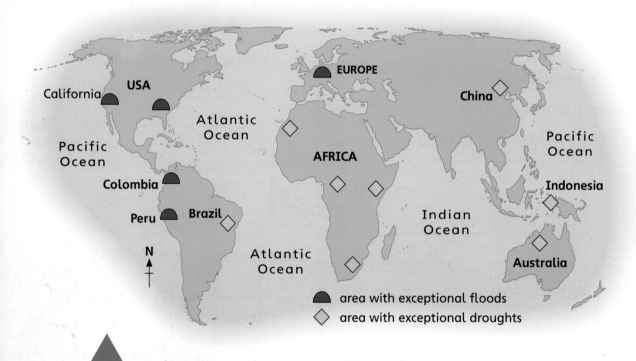

Changes in the weather caused by El Niño. **Droughts** are shown in yellow, and floods are shown in blue.

These wild animals were killed by **drought** in Australia.

In parts of Europe and America, too much rain falls. Rivers overflow, and there are floods. Water rushes through the streets, and people have to leave their homes.

These people are leaving their homes to escape from flooding in the United States of America.

EDGEWATER

Rainforest fires

El Niño brings **drought** to many lands where rainforests grow. The forest trees and bushes become very dry. A single spark can set them on fire.

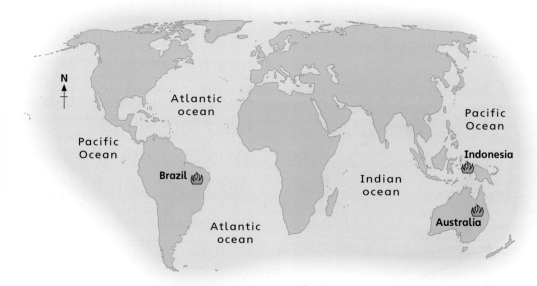

The orange flames show where forest fires break out in El Niño years.

This fire destroyed a huge area of rainforest in Queensland, Australia.

Rainforest fires cause serious damage to the **environment**. Many plants and animals are killed.

Labels: Amazon Grey Parrot, Anaconda, Hummingbird, Borneo Bearded Pig, Cayman, Jaguar, Giant Longhorn Beetle, Orang-utan, Komodo Dragon

▲ All this wildlife may die out because of forest fires.

Smoke from burning forests causes dangerous air pollution. People living near the forest fires become ill.

Clouds of smoke from nearby forest fires made the air in the Kalimantan region of Indonesia very dangerous to breathe in 1998. ▶

Hurricanes

Scientists also think that El Niño causes terrifying storms over the Atlantic and Pacific Oceans. These storms are called hurricanes or typhoons.

A swirling hurricane storm seen from space. ▶

Hurricane winds bring strong winds and rain.

▼

Hurricane winds swirl round and round very fast. They can reach 160 km per hour. When they reach the land, they smash trees and rip the roofs off buildings. They wreck shops, homes and schools.

Damage caused by a hurricane in Darwin, Australia.

Hurricanes mean disaster for many families. This house in Florida, United States of America, was destroyed by Hurricane Andrew.

An El Niño mystery

For the past 20 years, the world's weather has been changing. The weather has got hotter in many countries. People call this "global warming".

Global warming has caused many glaciers to melt and shrink.

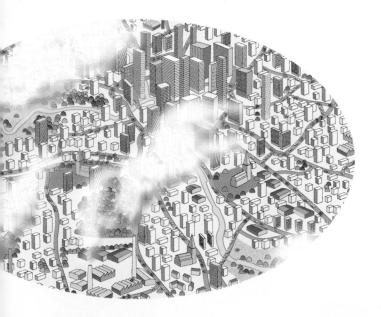

Some scientists think that gases from cars, fires and factories have caused global warming. They think we should control these gases, to stop the weather changing any more.

The weather has also been changing in El Niño years. The floods, droughts and hurricanes have all got much worse.

Some people think this has been caused by global warming, but no one knows for sure. Scientists are working to solve this mystery.

This is Rhoka village in Kenya. El Niño caused a flood here in 1987.

Information about the **temperature** of the sea is sent from weather **buoys** to these computers.

Glossary

buoy A weather buoy is a float which is fixed to the bottom of the sea by ropes. It has instruments attached to it for recording information about the weather.

current A current is a body of water which moves in one direction.

drought A long spell of dry weather is called a drought.

environment The natural world.

fog Fog is made up of millions of tiny drops of water.

plankton Tiny animals which live in water. They are too small for you to see.

temperature A measure of how hot or cold it is.

Index